SPMG

SHM 1

Scottish Heinemann Maths

Check-ups

Name _____

Colour ☐ 3 red.   Colour ☐ 2 blue.

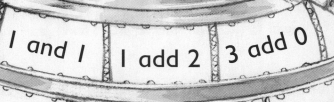

1 and 1   1 add 2   3 add 0

2 + 0   2 + 1   0 + 4   0 + 3

Make 5.

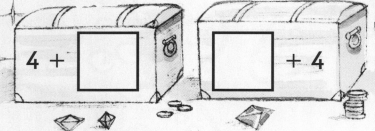

4 + ☐   ☐ + 4   3 + ☐   ☐ + 5

3 and 1 = ☐   1 add 0 = ☐   2 add 2 = ☐

5 + 0 = ☐   1 + 3 = ☐   0 + 1 = ☐

3 + ☐ = 5   ☐ + 0 = 4   0 + ☐ = 2

3 + 2 + 0 = ☐   1 + 1 + 2 = ☐   1 + 3 + 1 = ☐

$4 + 2 =$ ☐ $1 + 6 =$ ☐ $3 + 3 =$ ☐

$4 + 3 =$ ☐ $6 + 0 =$ ☐ $5 + 2 =$ ☐

$3 + 4 =$ ☐ $0 + 7 =$ ☐ $1 + 5 =$ ☐

Make 6.

$5 +$ ☐ $2 +$ ☐

☐ $+ 6$

Make 7.

$7 +$ ☐   ☐ $+ 1$

☐ $+ 5$

Colour ☐ 6 red.   Colour ☐ 7 blue.

3 add 4	1 add 6	4 and 2	0 and 7
4 + 3	1 add 5	5 add 2	0 + 6
1 + 2 + 3	2 add 4	5 + 1	3 + 3 + 1

Tick (✓) three ◯ to make 6.   Tick (✓) three ◯ to make 7.

(1) (4) (2) (3)   (1) (5) (3) (1) (2)

6 + 2 =

2 + 7 =

8 + 1 =

9 + 0 =

4 + 4 =

1 + 7 =

5 + 2 =

6 + 3 =

0 + 8 =

2 + 6 =

4 + 5 =

3 + 3 =

 Make 8.

 Make 9.

3   add   ☐

☐   +   1

☐   add   ☐

7   +   ☐

☐   add   4

☐   add   ☐

1 + 2 + 6 =

1 + 4 + 3 =

1 + 7 + 0 =

0 + 1 + 8 =

9 + 1 = ☐

6 add 2 = ☐

5 + 5 = ☐

2 + 7 = ☐

10 add 0 = ☐

7 + 3 = ☐

8 + ☐ = 10

3 + ☐ = 9

0 + ☐ = 10

☐ + 9 = 10

☐ + 4 = 10

Colour  10 .

3 add 7

4 + 6

2 + 4 + 3

1 + 8

3 + 4 + 1

2 add 8

Tick (✓) two  to make 10.

 1    7    2    3

Tick (✓) three  to make 10.

 2   1    2    6    3

Write the missing numbers.

| 16 | 17 | | |

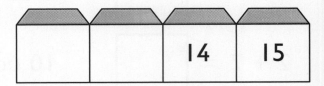

| | | 14 | 15 |

Write the number

before 11 ☐   after 19   before 16

after 18   before 14 ☐   after 17 ☐

Match

the number

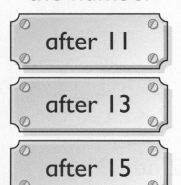

after 11

after 13

after 15

14

12

16

the number

before 15

before 17

before 13

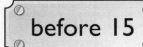

Write the number between

12 and 14 ☐   13 and 15 ☐

20 and 18 ☐   16 and 14 ☐

Write **one** number between 12 and 17. ☐

Tick (✓) the larger number.

Tick (✓) the smaller number.

Colour the largest number.

Colour the smallest number.

Write the numbers in order.

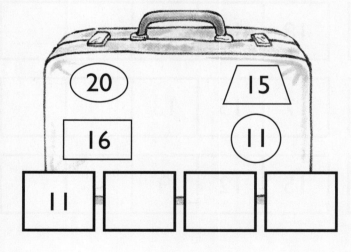

| 11 | | | |

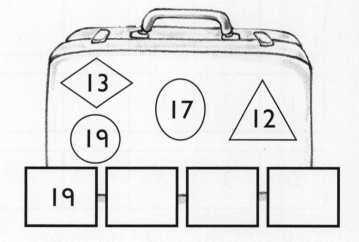

| 19 | | | |

1 more than 14 ⟶ ☐

2 less than 13 ⟶ ☐

2 more than 18 ⟶ ☐

2 less than 19 ⟶ ☐

2 more than 10 ⟶ ☐

1 less than 15 ⟶ ☐

Join in order. Colour.

16 18

14•   20

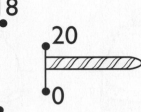

0

•9

12• •6

4

8   6

2

•15

18• •3

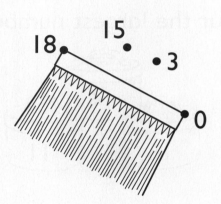

0

12 10

Write the missing numbers.

2	4	6		

18	16	14		

1	3	5		

17	15	13		

0	3	6		

15	12	9		

Tick (✓) the even numbers.

2   3   6   9   12   16   19

Tick (✓) the odd numbers.

1   4   7   9   11   14   20

Write the numbers.

nineteen ☐   eleven ☐   thirteen ☐

fifteen ☐   twenty ☐   fourteen ☐

Match.

17

sixteen

12

twelve

16

seventeen

Colour the seventh 3rd first 9th .

2 – 1 = ☐   4 – 4 = ☐   5 – 1 = ☐

4 – 3 = ☐   2 – 0 = ☐   5 – 5 = ☐

3 – 0 = ☐   3 – 2 = ☐   4 – 0 = ☐

Hide 2.
How many are left? ___

Hide 3.
How many are left? ___

4 less than 5 = ☐   5 subtract 0 = ☐

Subtract 1 from 3. ☐   Take 2 from 2. ☐

2 + 3 = ☐   3 + 2 = ☐

5 – 3 = ☐   5 – 2 = ☐

8 – 7 = ☐   8 – 2 = ☐   8 – 0 = ☐

7 – 1 = ☐   7 – 0 = ☐   7 – 3 = ☐

6 – 4 = ☐   6 – 1 = ☐   6 – 6 = ☐

8 – 3 = ☐   7 – 4 = ☐   6 – 5 = ☐

Match.

 8 – 6

 7 – 2

6 – 3

6   4   2   3   5   0

 6 – 0

 8 – 4

 7 – 7

8 take away 5 = ☐   7 subtract 6 = ☐

Take 1 from 8. ☐   Take 2 from 6. ☐

Subtract 5 from 7. ☐   Subtract 5 from 6. ☐

9 – 5 = ☐   10 – 0 = ☐   9 – 8 = ☐

10 – 9 = ☐   9 – 7 = ☐   10 – 6 = ☐

9 – 0 = ☐   10 – 4 = ☐   9 – 9 = ☐

Match.

(9 – 7)   (10 – 8)   (10 – 5)   (9 – 9)   (9 – 2)

[2]   [8]   [0]   [5]   [7]

(10 – 2)   (10 – 10)   (9 – 1)   (10 – 3)   (9 – 4)

3 fly away.
How many are left? ☐

6 are sold.
How many are left? ☐

10 subtract 7 = ☐   9 take away 8 = ☐

6 less than 9 = ☐   Take 4 from 10. ☐

Subtraction to 10: pages 23–27

 How many more ? _____

□ − □ =

Find the difference between

2 and 8 _____   10 and 5 _____

Complete.

□ − □ = 4   □ − □ = 0

3 + 6 =

6 + 3 =

9 − 3 =

9 − 6 =

5 + 2 = 7

＿ + 5 = 7

＿ − 5 = 2

7 − ＿ = 5

6 − □ = 5   □ − 2 = 7

10 − □ = 8   □ − 4 = 4

1 Write the number

after 13 ☐   before 16 ☐

between 17 and 19 ☐ .

2 Write the numbers in order.

(15) (9) (20) (12) (16)

<u>9</u> ___ ___ ___ ___

3

2 + 5 = ☐   4 + 4 = ☐   5 + 3 = ☐

6 + 0 = ☐   2 + 3 = ☐   8 + 1 = ☐

4   Make 10.

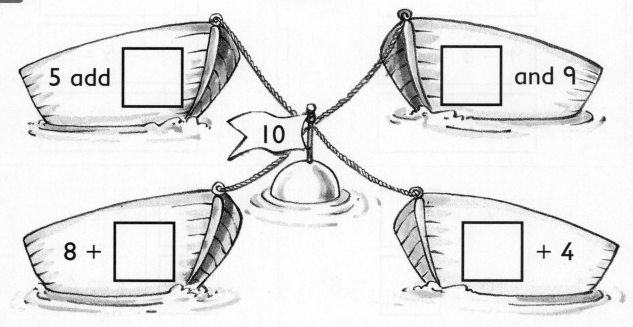

5 add ☐

☐ and 9

8 + ☐

☐ + 4

10

5 How many altogether?

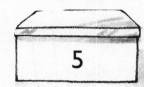 5   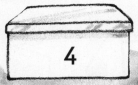 4   [ ]

6

7 − 3 = [ ]   10 − 5 = [ ]   9 − 8 = [ ]

5 − 2 = [ ]   6 − 4 = [ ]   8 − 5 = [ ]

7

_____ balloons.
3 blow away.
How many are left? _____

[− =]

8

 10   6

How many more ? _____

[− =]

9

7 + 2 = 9

[ ] + 7 = 9

[ ] − 2 = 7

9 − [ ] = 2

10 Make £1 less.   Make £2 more.

11 Tick (✓) coins to buy.

12 Match.

square

circle

triangle

13 Draw a tall .   Draw a short .

14   Match.

6 o'clock

1 o'clock

11 o'clock

6:00

15 Sort the numbers.   ~~9~~   ~~3~~   10   2   6   8   7

less than 7   ~~less than 7~~

5   9

1 Match.

| 14 | 12 | 20 | 15 |

twelve   fourteen   fifteen   twenty

2 Tick (✓) the 2nd and last .

3

7 + 3 = ☐   6 + 2 = ☐   1 + 8 = ☐

3 + 4 + 2 = ☐   1 + 5 + 4 = ☐

4

3 + ☐ = 8   ☐ add 2 = 9

5 + ☐ = 5   ☐ and 7 = 8

5 Make 6.

☐ and ☐

Make 7.

☐ + ☐ + ☐

6

7 take away 6 = ☐

2 less than 8 = ☐

Subtract 0 from 9. ☐

Take 4 from 10. ☐

7 Find the difference between

2 and 10 ☐

5 and 6 ☐

8 and 1 ☐

8

7 are sold.
How many are left? ——

☐ – ☐ = ☐

9

$9 - ☐ = 3$

$☐ - 5 = 0$

$10 - ☐ = 10$

$☐ - 3 = 1$

10 How much?

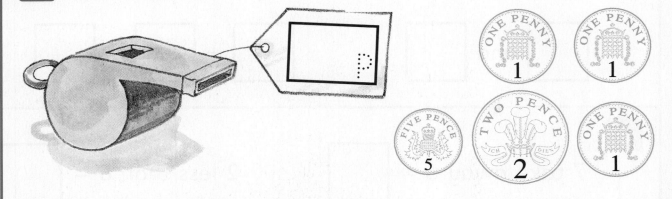

11 How much altogether?

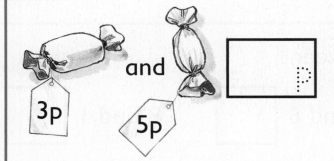 and [   ]p

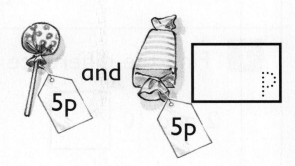 and [   ]p

2p + 4p = [   ]p

6p + 3p = [   ]p

12 £7

Buy

£5

How much is left? £[   ]

£8 − £6 = £[   ]

£10 − £7 = £[   ]

Sorting and matching

Sorting | PS 1 | PS 2 | PS 3 | PS 4 | PS 5 | PS 6 | PS 7 | PS 8

Matching

Numbers to 10

One and two | PS 9

Three | PS 10 | AB 1 | AB 2 | PS 11 | AB 3

Four | PS 11 | AB 4 | AB 5 | AB 6

Five | PS 12 | AB 7 | AB 8 | AB 9

Ordering to 5 | PS 13 | AB 10 | AB 11 | AB 12

Six and seven | PS 14 | PS 15 | AB 13 | AB 14 | AB 15 | AB 16

Eight and nine | PS 16 | AB 17 | AB 18 | AB 19 | AB 20

Ten | PS 17 | AB 21 | AB 22 | AB 23

Ordering to 10 | PS 17 | AB 24 | AB 25 | PS 18 | AB 26 | PS 19 | AB 27 | PS 19 | AB 28 | AB 29

Numbers to 20

Patterns | AB 30 | AB 31

Record of work: SHM 1

Addition to 10

Concept of addition	PS 20	AB 1	AB 2	PS 21	AB 3	AB 4

Recording addition	AB 5	PS 22	AB 6	AB 7

Adding 1 and 2	AB 8	AB 9

Addition facts to 5	AB 10	AB 11	AB 12

Consolidation of addition facts to 5	PS 22	AB 13

Assessment	AB 14

Addition to 5: consolidation	PS 23	PS 24	PS 25	AB 15	AB 16	HA 1	CU 1

Doubles and near doubles	PS 26	AB 17	PS 27	AB 18

Addition facts for 6 and 7	AB 19	AB 20	HA 2	AB 21	AB 22	PS 28	PS 29	PS 30	CU 2

Addition facts for 8 and 9	PS 30	AB 23	AB 24	HA 3	PS 30	PS 31	AB 25	AB 26	CU 3

Addition facts to 10	PS 32	AB 27	AB 28	AB 29	HA 4	CU 4

Assessment	AB 30	AB 31

Numbers to 20

Number sequence to 20	AB 1	AB 2	AB 3	AB 4	AB 5	AB 6	HA 5	CU 5

Counting to 20	PS 33	AB 7	AB 8	AB 9	PS 34	AB 10	HA 6

Comparing and ordering numbers	PS 35	PS 36	AB 11	AB 12	PS 37	AB 13	HA 7	AB 14	HA 8	CU 6

Even and odd numbers	PS 38	PS 39	AB 15	PS 38	PS 39	AB 16	PS 38	AB 17	HA 9	CU 7

Number names	AB 18	AB 19	AB 20	HA 10	CU 8

Ordinal numbers	

Assessment	AB 21	AB 22	AB 23

Subtraction to 10

Concept of subtraction	AB 1	PS 40	AB 2

Subtraction involving 1, 2 and 0	AB 3	HA 11	AB 4

Subtraction facts to 5	AB 5	PS 41	AB 6	PS 42	AB 7	HA 12

Subtraction language	AB 8	HA 13	AB 9	AB 10	HA 14	AB 11	CU 9

Assessment	AB 12

Subtraction within 10	AB 13	HA 15	AB 14	AB 15	PS 43	AB 16	AB 17

Facts for 6 and 7	AB 18	HA 16	AB 19	AB 20	HA 17

Facts for 8 and 9	AB 21	AB 22	HA 18	CU 10	AB 23	AB 24	HA 19

Facts for 10	AB 25	AB 26	PS 44	HA 20	HA 21	AB 27	PS 45	CU 11

Subtraction: comparison	AB 28	AB 29	HA 22	PS 46	AB 30	PS 47

Linking + and − facts for 6 to 10	AB 31	AB 32	AB 33	AB 34	AB 35

Subtraction to 10	AB 36	AB 37	CU 12

Assessment	AB 38	AB 39

Money

Recognising coins	PS 48

Addition to 10p/£10	AB 1	PS 49	PS 50	AB 2	AB 3

Subtraction within 10p/£10	AB 4	AB 5	AB 6

Using 1p, 2p and 5p coins	PS 51	PS 52	PS 53	AB 7	AB 8	AB 9	AB 10	HA 22

Assessment	AB 11	AB 12

Record of work: SHM 1

Shape

3D Shape	PS 54	PS 55

Position and movement	

2D Shape	PS 56	PS 57

Measure

Length	PS 58	PS 59

Weight	

Capacity	

Time: days of the week	

Time: telling the time	PS 60	AB 13	AB 14	AB 15

Data Handling

Sorting, matching, relationships	PS 5	PS 6	PS 7	AB 16	PS 61	AB 17	AB 18	PS 62	PS 63	PS 64

Bar graphs	PS 65	AB 19	AB 20	PS 66	AB 21	AB 22	AB 23

Round-up 1

1	2	3	4	5	6	7	8	9	10	11	12	13	14	15

Round-up 2

1	2	3	4	5	6	7	8	9	10	11	12

Heinemann is an imprint of Pearson Education Limited, a company incorporated in England and Wales, having its registered office at Edinburgh Gate, Harlow, Essex, CM20 2JE.
Registered company number: 872828
ISBN 978 0435 168759   © Scottish Primary Mathematics Group 1999.
First published 1999.   10   13
Designed and illustrated by Gecko Ltd.
Printed in Malaysia, (CTP-PPSB)

ISBN 978-0-435168-75-9

9 780435 168759